planning pages®

MOM'S PLANNER

ORGANIZING ESSENTIALS

KAHOOTIE CO®
www.kahootie.com

Sunday	Monday	Tuesday	Wednesday

Thursday	Friday	Saturday	

Sunday	Monday	Tuesday	Wednesday

Thursday	Friday	Saturday	

Sunday	Monday	Tuesday	Wednesday

Thursday	Friday	Saturday

Sunday	Monday	Tuesday	Wednesday

Sunday	Monday	Tuesday	Wednesday

Thursday	Friday	Saturday	

Sunday	Monday	Tuesday	Wednesday

Thursday	Friday	Saturday	

Sunday	Monday	Tuesday	Wednesday

Thursday	Friday	Saturday

Sunday	Monday	Tuesday	Wednesday

Sunday	Monday	Tuesday	Wednesday

Sunday	Monday	Tuesday	Wednesday

Thursday	Friday	Saturday

Sunday	Monday	Tuesday	Wednesday

Thursday	Friday	Saturday

KAHOOTIE CO.

Sunday	Monday	Tuesday	Wednesday

Thursday	Friday	Saturday	

KAHOOTIE CO.

Monday /

_____ : _____   _____
_____ : _____   _____
_____ : _____   _____
_____ : _____   _____
_____ : _____   _____

Tuesday /

_____ : _____   _____
_____ : _____   _____
_____ : _____   _____
_____ : _____   _____
_____ : _____   _____

Wednesday /

_____ : _____   _____
_____ : _____   _____
_____ : _____   _____
_____ : _____   _____
_____ : _____   _____

Thursday /

_____ : _____   _____
_____ : _____   _____
_____ : _____   _____
_____ : _____   _____

Friday /

_____ : _____   _____
_____ : _____   _____
_____ : _____   _____
_____ : _____   _____
_____ : _____   _____

Mom's Goals :

_____
_____
_____

Kid's Goals :

_____
_____
_____

Top 4 To-Do :

Meal Planner

1 _____
2 _____
3 _____
4 _____

Mon

Tue

_____
_____
_____
_____
_____
_____
_____
_____
_____
_____
_____
_____
_____

Wed

Thu

Fri

Sat

Sun

Weekend

Saturday

_____
_____
_____
_____

Sunday

_____
_____
_____
_____

Monday /

_____ : _____ _____

_____ : _____ _____

_____ : _____ _____

_____ : _____ _____

_____ : _____ _____

Tuesday /

_____ : _____ _____

_____ : _____ _____

_____ : _____ _____

_____ : _____ _____

_____ : _____ _____

Wednesday /

_____ : _____ _____

_____ : _____ _____

_____ : _____ _____

_____ : _____ _____

Thursday /

_____ : _____ _____

_____ : _____ _____

_____ : _____ _____

_____ : _____ _____

_____ : _____ _____

Friday /

_____ : _____ _____

_____ : _____ _____

_____ : _____ _____

_____ : _____ _____

_____ : _____ _____

Mom's Goals :

_____
_____
_____

Kid's Goals :

_____
_____
_____

Top 4 To-Do :

1 _____
2 _____
3 _____
4 _____

_____
_____
_____
_____
_____
_____
_____
_____
_____
_____

Meal Planner

Mon

Tue

Wed

Thu

Fri

Sat

Sun

Weekend

Saturday

_____
_____
_____
_____
_____

Sunday

_____
_____
_____
_____
_____

KAHOOTIE CO.

Monday   /

_____ : _____   _____
_____ : _____   _____
_____ : _____   _____
_____ : _____   _____
_____ : _____   _____

Tuesday   /

_____ : _____   _____
_____ : _____   _____
_____ : _____   _____
_____ : _____   _____
_____ : _____   _____

Wednesday   /

_____ : _____   _____
_____ : _____   _____
_____ : _____   _____
_____ : _____   _____
_____ : _____   _____

Thursday   /

_____ : _____   _____
_____ : _____   _____
_____ : _____   _____
_____ : _____   _____
_____ : _____   _____

Friday   /

_____ : _____   _____
_____ : _____   _____
_____ : _____   _____
_____ : _____   _____
_____ : _____   _____

Mom's Goals :

_____
_____
_____

Kid's Goals :

_____
_____
_____

Top 4 To-Do :

Meal Planner

1 _____
2 _____
3 _____
4 _____

Mon

Tue

_____
_____

Wed

_____
_____

Thu

_____
_____

Fri

_____
_____

Sat

_____
_____

Sun

Weekend

Saturday

_____
_____
_____
_____
_____

Sunday

_____
_____
_____
_____
_____

Monday /

_____ : _____   _____

_____ : _____   _____

_____ : _____   _____

_____ : _____   _____

_____ : _____   _____

Tuesday /

_____ : _____   _____

_____ : _____   _____

_____ : _____   _____

_____ : _____   _____

_____ : _____   _____

Wednesday /

_____ : _____   _____

_____ : _____   _____

_____ : _____   _____

_____ : _____   _____

_____ : _____   _____

Thursday /

_____ : _____   _____

_____ : _____   _____

_____ : _____   _____

_____ : _____   _____

_____ : _____   _____

Friday /

_____ : _____   _____

_____ : _____   _____

_____ : _____   _____

_____ : _____   _____

_____ : _____   _____

Mom's Goals :

_____

_____

_____

Kid's Goals :

_____

_____

_____

Top 4 To-Do :

Meal Planner

1 _____

2 _____

Mon

3 _____

4 _____

Tue

_____

_____

Wed

_____

_____

Thu

_____

_____

Fri

_____

_____

Sat

_____

_____

Sun

_____

_____

Weekend

Saturday

Sunday

_____   _____

_____   _____

_____   _____

_____   _____

_____   _____

Monday /

_____ : _____

_____ : _____

_____ : _____

_____ : _____

_____ : _____

Tuesday /

_____ : _____

_____ : _____

_____ : _____

_____ : _____

_____ : _____

Wednesday /

_____ : _____

_____ : _____

_____ : _____

_____ : _____

_____ : _____

Thursday /

_____ : _____

_____ : _____

_____ : _____

_____ : _____

_____ : _____

Friday /

_____ : _____

_____ : _____

_____ : _____

_____ : _____

_____ : _____

Mom's Goals :

_____

_____

_____

Kid's Goals :

_____

_____

_____

Top 4 To-Do :

1 _____

2 _____

3 _____

4 _____

_____

_____

_____

_____

_____

_____

_____

_____

_____

_____

_____

Meal Planner

Mon

Tue

Wed

Thu

Fri

Sat

Sun

Weekend

Saturday

_____

_____

_____

_____

Sunday

_____

_____

_____

_____

Monday /

_____ : _____   _____
_____ : _____   _____
_____ : _____   _____
_____ : _____   _____
_____ : _____   _____

Tuesday /

_____ : _____   _____
_____ : _____   _____
_____ : _____   _____
_____ : _____   _____
_____ : _____   _____

Wednesday /

_____ : _____   _____
_____ : _____   _____
_____ : _____   _____
_____ : _____   _____
_____ : _____   _____

Thursday /

_____ : _____   _____
_____ : _____   _____
_____ : _____   _____
_____ : _____   _____

Friday /

_____ : _____   _____
_____ : _____   _____
_____ : _____   _____
_____ : _____   _____
_____ : _____   _____

Mom's Goals :

_____

_____

_____

Kid's Goals :

_____

_____

_____

Top 4 To-Do :

1 _____

2 _____

3 _____

4 _____

_____

_____

_____

_____

_____

_____

_____

_____

_____

_____

_____

_____

Meal Planner

Mon

Tue

Wed

Thu

Fri

Sat

Sun

Weekend

Saturday

_____

_____

_____

_____

Sunday

_____

_____

_____

_____

KAHOOTIE CO.

Monday   /

_____ : _____   _____

_____ : _____   _____

_____ : _____   _____

_____ : _____   _____

_____ : _____   _____

Tuesday   /

_____ : _____   _____

_____ : _____   _____

_____ : _____   _____

_____ : _____   _____

_____ : _____   _____

Wednesday   /

_____ : _____   _____

_____ : _____   _____

_____ : _____   _____

_____ : _____   _____

_____ : _____   _____

Thursday   /

_____ : _____   _____

_____ : _____   _____

_____ : _____   _____

_____ : _____   _____

_____ : _____   _____

Friday   /

_____ : _____   _____

_____ : _____   _____

_____ : _____   _____

_____ : _____   _____

_____ : _____   _____

Mom's Goals :

_____

_____

_____

Kid's Goals :

_____

_____

_____

Top 4 To-Do :

1 _____

2 _____

3 _____

4 _____

_____

_____

_____

_____

_____

_____

_____

_____

_____

Meal Planner

Mon

Tue

Wed

Thu

Fri

Sat

Sun

Weekend

Saturday

_____

_____

_____

_____

Sunday

_____

_____

_____

_____

Monday /

_____ : _____ _____

_____ : _____ _____

_____ : _____ _____

_____ : _____ _____

_____ : _____ _____

Tuesday /

_____ : _____ _____

_____ : _____ _____

_____ : _____ _____

_____ : _____ _____

_____ : _____ _____

Wednesday /

_____ : _____ _____

_____ : _____ _____

_____ : _____ _____

_____ : _____ _____

_____ : _____ _____

Thursday /

_____ : _____ _____

_____ : _____ _____

_____ : _____ _____

_____ : _____ _____

_____ : _____ _____

Friday /

_____ : _____ _____

_____ : _____ _____

_____ : _____ _____

_____ : _____ _____

_____ : _____ _____

Mom's Goals :

_____
_____
_____

Kid's Goals :

_____
_____
_____

Top 4 To-Do :

1 _____
2 _____
3 _____
4 _____

_____
_____
_____
_____
_____
_____
_____
_____
_____
_____
_____
_____

Meal Planner

Mon

Tue

Wed

Thu

Fri

Sat

Sun

Weekend

Saturday

_____
_____
_____
_____

Sunday

_____
_____
_____
_____

Monday   /

____ : _____   _____
____ : _____   _____
____ : _____   _____
____ : _____   _____
____ : _____

Tuesday   /

____ : _____   _____
____ : _____   _____
____ : _____   _____
____ : _____   _____
____ : _____

Wednesday   /

____ : _____   _____
____ : _____   _____
____ : _____   _____
____ : _____   _____
____ : _____   _____

Thursday   /

____ : _____   _____
____ : _____   _____
____ : _____   _____
____ : _____   _____
____ : _____

Friday   /

____ : _____   _____
____ : _____   _____
____ : _____   _____
____ : _____   _____

Mom's Goals :

_____

_____

_____

Kid's Goals :

_____

_____

_____

Top 4 To-Do :

Meal Planner

1 _____

2 _____   Mon

3 _____

4 _____   Tue

_____

_____   Wed

_____

_____   Thu

_____

_____   Fri

_____

_____   Sat

_____

_____   Sun

_____

Weekend

Saturday   Sunday

_____   _____

_____   _____

_____   _____

_____   _____

Monday   /

_____ : _____   _____
_____ : _____   _____
_____ : _____   _____
_____ : _____   _____
_____ : _____   _____

Tuesday   /

_____ : _____   _____
_____ : _____   _____
_____ : _____   _____
_____ : _____   _____
_____ : _____   _____

Wednesday   /

_____ : _____   _____
_____ : _____   _____
_____ : _____   _____
_____ : _____   _____
_____ : _____   _____

Thursday   /

_____ : _____   _____
_____ : _____   _____
_____ : _____   _____
_____ : _____   _____
_____ : _____   _____

Friday   /

_____ : _____   _____
_____ : _____   _____
_____ : _____   _____
_____ : _____   _____
_____ : _____   _____

Mom's Goals :

_____

_____

_____

Kid's Goals :

_____

_____

_____

Top 4 To-Do :

1 _____

2 _____

3 _____

4 _____

_____

_____

_____

_____

_____

_____

_____

_____

_____

_____

_____

_____

Meal Planner

Mon

Tue

Wed

Thu

Fri

Sat

Sun

Weekend

Saturday

_____

_____

_____

_____

Sunday

_____

_____

_____

_____

Monday /

_____ : _____

_____ : _____

_____ : _____

_____ : _____

_____ : _____

Tuesday /

_____ : _____

_____ : _____

_____ : _____

_____ : _____

_____ : _____

Wednesday /

_____ : _____

_____ : _____

_____ : _____

_____ : _____

_____ : _____

Thursday /

_____ : _____

_____ : _____

_____ : _____

_____ : _____

_____ : _____

Friday /

_____ : _____

_____ : _____

_____ : _____

_____ : _____

_____ : _____

Mom's Goals :

_____

_____

_____

Kid's Goals :

_____

_____

_____

Top 4 To-Do :

1 _____

2 _____

3 _____

4 _____

_____

_____

_____

_____

_____

_____

_____

_____

_____

_____

_____

_____

_____

Meal Planner

Mon

Tue

Wed

Thu

Fri

Sat

Sun

Weekend

Saturday

_____

_____

_____

_____

_____

Sunday

_____

_____

_____

_____

_____

KAHOOTIE CO.

Monday   /

_____ : _____   _____
_____ : _____   _____
_____ : _____   _____
_____ : _____   _____
_____ : _____   _____

Tuesday   /

_____ : _____   _____
_____ : _____   _____
_____ : _____   _____
_____ : _____   _____
_____ : _____   _____

Wednesday   /

_____ : _____   _____
_____ : _____   _____
_____ : _____   _____
_____ : _____   _____
_____ : _____   _____

Thursday   /

_____ : _____   _____
_____ : _____   _____
_____ : _____   _____
_____ : _____   _____
_____ : _____   _____

Friday   /

_____ : _____   _____
_____ : _____   _____
_____ : _____   _____
_____ : _____   _____
_____ : _____   _____

Mom's Goals :

_____
_____
_____

Kid's Goals :

_____
_____
_____

Top 4 To-Do :

1 _____
2 _____
3 _____
4 _____

_____
_____
_____
_____
_____
_____
_____
_____
_____
_____
_____

Meal Planner

Mon

Tue

Wed

Thu

Fri

Sat

Sun

Weekend

Saturday

_____
_____
_____
_____
_____

Sunday

_____
_____
_____
_____
_____

KAHOOTIE CO.

Monday /

_____ : _____   _____

_____ : _____   _____

_____ : _____   _____

_____ : _____   _____

_____ : _____

Tuesday /

_____ : _____   _____

_____ : _____   _____

_____ : _____   _____

_____ : _____   _____

_____ : _____

Wednesday /

_____ : _____   _____

_____ : _____   _____

_____ : _____   _____

_____ : _____   _____

_____ : _____   _____

Thursday /

_____ : _____   _____

_____ : _____   _____

_____ : _____   _____

_____ : _____   _____

_____ : _____   _____

Friday /

_____ : _____   _____

_____ : _____   _____

_____ : _____   _____

_____ : _____   _____

_____ : _____   _____

Mom's Goals :

_____

_____

_____

Kid's Goals :

_____

_____

_____

Top 4 To-Do :

1 _____

2 _____

3 _____

4 _____

☐ _____

☐ _____

☐ _____

☐ _____

☐ _____

☐ _____

☐ _____

☐ _____

☐ _____

☐ _____

☐ _____

Meal Planner

Mon

Tue

Wed

Thu

Fri

Sat

Sun

Weekend

Saturday

_____

_____

_____

_____

Sunday

_____

_____

_____

_____

KAHOOTIE CO.

Monday   /

_____ : _____   _____
_____ : _____   _____
_____ : _____   _____
_____ : _____   _____
_____ : _____   _____

Tuesday   /

_____ : _____   _____
_____ : _____   _____
_____ : _____   _____
_____ : _____   _____
_____ : _____   _____

Wednesday   /

_____ : _____   _____
_____ : _____   _____
_____ : _____   _____
_____ : _____   _____
_____ : _____   _____

Thursday   /

_____ : _____   _____
_____ : _____   _____
_____ : _____   _____
_____ : _____   _____
_____ : _____   _____

Friday   /

_____ : _____   _____
_____ : _____   _____
_____ : _____   _____
_____ : _____   _____
_____ : _____   _____

Mom's Goals :

_____

_____

_____

Kid's Goals :

_____

_____

_____

Top 4 To-Do :

1 _____

2 _____

3 _____

4 _____

_____

_____

_____

_____

_____

_____

_____

_____

_____

_____

_____

_____

Meal Planner

Mon

Tue

Wed

Thu

Fri

Sat

Sun

Weekend

Saturday

_____

_____

_____

_____

_____

Sunday

_____

_____

_____

_____

_____

KAHOOTIE CO.

Monday /

_____ : _____ _____

_____ : _____ _____

_____ : _____ _____

_____ : _____ _____

_____ : _____ _____

Tuesday /

_____ : _____ _____

_____ : _____ _____

_____ : _____ _____

_____ : _____ _____

_____ : _____ _____

Wednesday /

_____ : _____ _____

_____ : _____ _____

_____ : _____ _____

_____ : _____ _____

_____ : _____ _____

Thursday /

_____ : _____ _____

_____ : _____ _____

_____ : _____ _____

_____ : _____ _____

Friday /

_____ : _____ _____

_____ : _____ _____

_____ : _____ _____

_____ : _____ _____

_____ : _____ _____

Mom's Goals :

_____

_____

_____

Kid's Goals :

_____

_____

_____

Top 4 To-Do :

1 _____
2 _____
3 _____
4 _____

_____

_____

_____

_____

_____

_____

_____

_____

_____

_____

_____

_____

Meal Planner

Mon

Tue

Wed

Thu

Fri

Sat

Sun

Weekend

Saturday

_____

_____

_____

_____

_____

Sunday

_____

_____

_____

_____

_____

KAHOOTIE CO.

Monday /

_____ : _____   _____

_____ : _____   _____

_____ : _____   _____

_____ : _____   _____

_____ : _____   _____

Tuesday /

_____ : _____   _____

_____ : _____   _____

_____ : _____   _____

_____ : _____   _____

_____ : _____   _____

Wednesday /

_____ : _____   _____

_____ : _____   _____

_____ : _____   _____

_____ : _____   _____

_____ : _____   _____

Thursday /

_____ : _____   _____

_____ : _____   _____

_____ : _____   _____

_____ : _____   _____

Friday /

_____ : _____   _____

_____ : _____   _____

_____ : _____   _____

_____ : _____   _____

_____ : _____   _____

Mom's Goals :

_____

_____

_____

Kid's Goals :

_____

_____

_____

Top 4 To-Do :

Meal Planner

1 _____

2 _____   Mon

3 _____

4 _____   Tue

_____   Wed

_____

_____   Thu

_____   Fri

_____

_____   Sat

_____

_____   Sun

_____

Weekend

Saturday

_____

_____

_____

_____

_____

Sunday

_____

_____

_____

_____

_____

Monday /

_____ : _____   _____

_____ : _____   _____

_____ : _____   _____

_____ : _____   _____

_____ : _____   _____

Tuesday /

_____ : _____   _____

_____ : _____   _____

_____ : _____   _____

_____ : _____   _____

_____ : _____   _____

Wednesday /

_____ : _____   _____

_____ : _____   _____

_____ : _____   _____

_____ : _____   _____

Thursday /

_____ : _____   _____

_____ : _____   _____

_____ : _____   _____

_____ : _____   _____

_____ : _____   _____

Friday /

_____ : _____   _____

_____ : _____   _____

_____ : _____   _____

_____ : _____   _____

_____ : _____   _____

Mom's Goals :

_____

_____

_____

Kid's Goals :

_____

_____

_____

Top 4 To-Do :

1 _____

2 _____

3 _____

4 _____

_____

_____

_____

_____

_____

_____

_____

_____

_____

_____

_____

_____

Meal Planner

Mon

Tue

Wed

Thu

Fri

Sat

Sun

Weekend

Saturday

_____

_____

_____

_____

_____

Sunday

_____

_____

_____

_____

_____

KAHOOTIE CO.

Monday   /

_____ : _____   _____

_____ : _____   _____

_____ : _____   _____

_____ : _____   _____

_____ : _____   _____

Tuesday   /

_____ : _____   _____

_____ : _____   _____

_____ : _____   _____

_____ : _____   _____

_____ : _____   _____

Wednesday   /

_____ : _____   _____

_____ : _____   _____

_____ : _____   _____

_____ : _____   _____

_____ : _____   _____

Thursday   /

_____ : _____   _____

_____ : _____   _____

_____ : _____   _____

_____ : _____   _____

_____ : _____   _____

Friday   /

_____ : _____   _____

_____ : _____   _____

_____ : _____   _____

_____ : _____   _____

_____ : _____   _____

Mom's Goals :

_____

_____

_____

Kid's Goals :

_____

_____

_____

Top 4 To-Do :

Meal Planner

1 _____

2 _____   Mon

3 _____

4 _____   Tue

_____

_____   Wed

_____

_____   Thu

_____

_____   Fri

_____

_____   Sat

_____

_____   Sun

_____

Weekend

Saturday   Sunday

_____   _____

_____   _____

_____   _____

_____   _____

_____   _____

Monday   /

_____ : _____   _____
_____ : _____   _____
_____ : _____   _____
_____ : _____   _____
_____ : _____   _____

Tuesday   /

_____ : _____   _____
_____ : _____   _____
_____ : _____   _____
_____ : _____   _____
_____ : _____   _____

Wednesday   /

_____ : _____   _____
_____ : _____   _____
_____ : _____   _____
_____ : _____   _____
_____ : _____   _____

Thursday   /

_____ : _____   _____
_____ : _____   _____
_____ : _____   _____
_____ : _____   _____
_____ : _____   _____

Friday   /

_____ : _____   _____
_____ : _____   _____
_____ : _____   _____
_____ : _____   _____
_____ : _____   _____

Mom's Goals :

_____

_____

_____

Kid's Goals :

_____

_____

_____

Top 4 To-Do :

1 _____

2 _____

3 _____

4 _____

_____

_____

_____

_____

_____

_____

_____

_____

_____

_____

_____

_____

_____

Meal Planner

Mon

Tue

Wed

Thu

Fri

Sat

Sun

Weekend

Saturday

_____

_____

_____

_____

_____

Sunday

_____

_____

_____

_____

_____

Monday /

_____ : _____   _____

_____ : _____   _____

_____ : _____   _____

_____ : _____   _____

_____ : _____   _____

Tuesday /

_____ : _____   _____

_____ : _____   _____

_____ : _____   _____

_____ : _____   _____

_____ : _____   _____

Wednesday /

_____ : _____   _____

_____ : _____   _____

_____ : _____   _____

_____ : _____   _____

_____ : _____   _____

Thursday /

_____ : _____   _____

_____ : _____   _____

_____ : _____   _____

_____ : _____   _____

Friday /

_____ : _____   _____

_____ : _____   _____

_____ : _____   _____

_____ : _____   _____

_____ : _____   _____

Mom's Goals :

_____
_____
_____

Kid's Goals :

_____
_____
_____

Top 4 To-Do :

1 _____
2 _____
3 _____
4 _____

_____
_____
_____
_____
_____
_____
_____
_____
_____
_____
_____
_____

Meal Planner

Mon

Tue

Wed

Thu

Fri

Sat

Sun

Weekend

Saturday

_____
_____
_____
_____

Sunday

_____
_____
_____
_____

Monday   /

_____ : _____   _____
_____ : _____   _____
_____ : _____   _____
_____ : _____   _____
_____ : _____   _____

Tuesday   /

_____ : _____   _____
_____ : _____   _____
_____ : _____   _____
_____ : _____   _____
_____ : _____   _____

Wednesday   /

_____   _____
_____ : _____   _____
_____ : _____   _____
_____ : _____   _____
_____ : _____   _____

Thursday   /

_____ : _____   _____
_____ : _____   _____
_____ : _____   _____
_____ : _____   _____
_____ : _____   _____

Friday   /

_____ : _____   _____
_____ : _____   _____
_____ : _____   _____
_____ : _____   _____
_____ : _____   _____

Mom's Goals :

_____

_____

_____

Kid's Goals :

_____

_____

_____

Top 4 To-Do :

1 _____

2 _____

3 _____

4 _____

_____

_____

_____

_____

_____

_____

_____

_____

_____

_____

_____

Meal Planner

Mon

Tue

Wed

Thu

Fri

Sat

Sun

Weekend

Saturday

_____

_____

_____

_____

Sunday

_____

_____

_____

_____

Monday   /

_____ : _____   _____
_____ : _____   _____
_____ : _____   _____
_____ : _____   _____
_____ : _____

Tuesday   /

_____ : _____   _____
_____ : _____   _____
_____ : _____   _____
_____ : _____   _____
_____ : _____

Wednesday   /

_____ : _____   _____
_____ : _____   _____
_____ : _____   _____
_____ : _____   _____

Thursday   /

_____ : _____   _____
_____ : _____   _____
_____ : _____   _____
_____ : _____   _____
_____ : _____   _____

Friday   /

_____ : _____   _____
_____ : _____   _____
_____ : _____   _____
_____ : _____   _____
_____ : _____   _____

Mom's Goals :

_____
_____
_____

Kid's Goals :

_____
_____
_____

Top 4 To-Do :

1 _____
2 _____
3 _____
4 _____

_____
_____
_____
_____
_____
_____
_____
_____
_____
_____

Meal Planner

Mon

Tue

Wed

Thu

Fri

Sat

Sun

Weekend

Saturday

_____
_____
_____
_____
_____

Sunday

_____
_____
_____
_____
_____

Monday /

_____ : _____

_____ : _____

_____ : _____

_____ : _____

_____ : _____

Tuesday /

_____ : _____

_____ : _____

_____ : _____

_____ : _____

Wednesday /

_____ : _____

_____ : _____

_____ : _____

_____ : _____

_____ : _____

Thursday /

_____ : _____

_____ : _____

_____ : _____

_____ : _____

Friday /

_____ : _____

_____ : _____

_____ : _____

_____ : _____

_____ : _____

Mom's Goals :

_____
_____
_____

Kid's Goals :

_____
_____
_____

Top 4 To-Do :

Meal Planner

1 _____

2 _____   Mon

3 _____

4 _____   Tue

_____

_____   Wed

_____

_____   Thu

_____

_____   Fri

_____

_____   Sat

_____

_____   Sun

_____

Weekend

Saturday

_____
_____
_____
_____
_____

Sunday

_____
_____
_____
_____
_____

Monday /

_____ : _____ _____

_____ : _____ _____

_____ : _____ _____

_____ : _____ _____

_____ : _____ _____

Tuesday /

_____ : _____ _____

_____ : _____ _____

_____ : _____ _____

_____ : _____ _____

_____ : _____ _____

Wednesday /

_____ : _____ _____

_____ : _____ _____

_____ : _____ _____

_____ : _____ _____

_____ : _____ _____

Thursday /

_____ : _____ _____

_____ : _____ _____

_____ : _____ _____

_____ : _____ _____

Friday /

_____ : _____ _____

_____ : _____ _____

_____ : _____ _____

_____ : _____ _____

_____ : _____ _____

Mom's Goals :

_____

_____

_____

Kid's Goals :

_____

_____

_____

Top 4 To-Do :

1 _____

2 _____

3 _____

4 _____

_____

_____

_____

_____

_____

_____

_____

_____

_____

_____

_____

Meal Planner

Mon

Tue

Wed

Thu

Fri

Sat

Sun

Weekend

Saturday

_____

_____

_____

_____

_____

Sunday

_____

_____

_____

_____

_____

Monday   /

_____ : _____   _____

_____ : _____   _____

_____ : _____   _____

_____ : _____   _____

_____ : _____

Tuesday   /

_____ : _____   _____

_____ : _____   _____

_____ : _____   _____

_____ : _____   _____

_____ : _____   _____

Wednesday   /

_____ : _____   _____

_____ : _____   _____

_____ : _____   _____

_____ : _____   _____

_____ : _____   _____

Thursday   /

_____ : _____   _____

_____ : _____   _____

_____ : _____   _____

_____ : _____   _____

_____ : _____   _____

Friday   /

_____ : _____   _____

_____ : _____   _____

_____ : _____   _____

_____ : _____   _____

_____ : _____   _____

Mom's Goals :

_____

_____

_____

Kid's Goals :

_____

_____

_____

Top 4 To-Do :

1 _____

2 _____

3 _____

4 _____

_____

_____

_____

_____

_____

_____

_____

_____

_____

_____

_____

Meal Planner

Mon

Tue

Wed

Thu

Fri

Sat

Sun

Weekend

Saturday

_____

_____

_____

_____

_____

Sunday

_____

_____

_____

_____

_____

Monday /

_____ : _____ _____

_____ : _____ _____

_____ : _____ _____

_____ : _____ _____

_____ : _____ _____

Tuesday /

_____ : _____ _____

_____ : _____ _____

_____ : _____ _____

_____ : _____ _____

_____ : _____ _____

Wednesday /

_____ : _____ _____

_____ : _____ _____

_____ : _____ _____

_____ : _____ _____

_____ : _____ _____

Thursday /

_____ : _____ _____

_____ : _____ _____

_____ : _____ _____

_____ : _____ _____

_____ : _____ _____

Friday /

_____ : _____ _____

_____ : _____ _____

_____ : _____ _____

_____ : _____ _____

_____ : _____ _____

Mom's Goals :

_____
_____
_____

Kid's Goals :

_____
_____
_____

Top 4 To-Do :

1 _____
2 _____
3 _____
4 _____

_____
_____
_____
_____
_____
_____
_____
_____
_____
_____
_____
_____

Meal Planner

Mon

Tue

Wed

Thu

Fri

Sat

Sun

Weekend

Saturday

_____
_____
_____
_____
_____

Sunday

_____
_____
_____
_____
_____

KAHOOTIE CO.

Monday /

_____ : _____

_____ : _____

_____ : _____

_____ : _____

_____ : _____

Tuesday /

_____ : _____

_____ : _____

_____ : _____

_____ : _____

_____ : _____

Wednesday /

_____ : _____

_____ : _____

_____ : _____

_____ : _____

Thursday /

_____ : _____

_____ : _____

_____ : _____

_____ : _____

Friday /

_____ : _____

_____ : _____

_____ : _____

_____ : _____

Mom's Goals :

_____

_____

_____

Kid's Goals :

_____

_____

_____

Top 4 To-Do :

1 _____

2 _____

3 _____

4 _____

_____

_____

_____

_____

_____

_____

_____

_____

_____

_____

_____

Meal Planner

Mon

Tue

Wed

Thu

Fri

Sat

Sun

Weekend

Saturday

_____

_____

_____

_____

_____

Sunday

_____

_____

_____

_____

_____

KAHOOTIE CO.

Monday /

_____ : _____   _____
_____ : _____   _____
_____ : _____   _____
_____ : _____   _____
_____ : _____   _____

Tuesday /

_____ : _____   _____
_____ : _____   _____
_____ : _____   _____
_____ : _____   _____
_____ : _____   _____

Wednesday /

_____ : _____   _____
_____ : _____   _____
_____ : _____   _____
_____ : _____   _____
_____ : _____   _____

Thursday /

_____ : _____   _____
_____ : _____   _____
_____ : _____   _____
_____ : _____   _____
_____ : _____   _____

Friday /

_____ : _____   _____
_____ : _____   _____
_____ : _____   _____
_____ : _____   _____
_____ : _____   _____

Mom's Goals :

_____

_____

_____

Kid's Goals :

_____

_____

_____

Top 4 To-Do :

1 _____

2 _____

3 _____

4 _____

_____

_____

_____

_____

_____

_____

_____

_____

_____

_____

_____

Meal Planner

Mon

Tue

Wed

Thu

Fri

Sat

Sun

Weekend

Saturday

_____

_____

_____

_____

Sunday

_____

_____

_____

_____

Monday   /

_____ : _____   _____
_____ : _____   _____
_____ : _____   _____
_____ : _____   _____
_____ : _____   _____

Tuesday   /

_____ : _____   _____
_____ : _____   _____
_____ : _____   _____
_____ : _____   _____
_____ : _____   _____

Wednesday   /

_____ : _____   _____
_____ : _____   _____
_____ : _____   _____
_____ : _____   _____

Thursday   /

_____ : _____   _____
_____ : _____   _____
_____ : _____   _____
_____ : _____   _____

Friday   /

_____ : _____   _____
_____ : _____   _____
_____ : _____   _____
_____ : _____   _____

Mom's Goals :

_____
_____
_____

Kid's Goals :

_____
_____
_____

Top 4 To-Do :

1 _____
2 _____
3 _____
4 _____

_____
_____
_____
_____
_____
_____
_____
_____
_____
_____
_____

Meal Planner

Mon

Tue

Wed

Thu

Fri

Sat

Sun

Weekend

Saturday

_____
_____
_____
_____
_____

Sunday

_____
_____
_____
_____
_____

Monday /

____ : _____ _____

____ : _____ _____

____ : _____ _____

____ : _____ _____

____ : _____ _____

Tuesday /

____ : _____ _____

____ : _____ _____

____ : _____ _____

____ : _____ _____

____ : _____ _____

Wednesday /

____ : _____ _____

____ : _____ _____

____ : _____ _____

____ : _____ _____

____ : _____ _____

Thursday /

____ : _____ _____

____ : _____ _____

____ : _____ _____

____ : _____ _____

____ : _____ _____

Friday /

____ : _____ _____

____ : _____ _____

____ : _____ _____

____ : _____ _____

____ : _____ _____

Mom's Goals :

_____
_____
_____

Kid's Goals :

_____
_____
_____

Top 4 To-Do :

1 _____
2 _____
3 _____
4 _____

_____
_____
_____
_____
_____
_____
_____
_____
_____
_____
_____
_____

Meal Planner

Mon

Tue

Wed

Thu

Fri

Sat

Sun

Weekend

Saturday

_____
_____
_____
_____
_____

Sunday

_____
_____
_____
_____
_____

KAHOOTIE CO.

Monday /

_____ : _____ _____
_____ : _____ _____
_____ : _____ _____
_____ : _____ _____
_____ : _____ _____

Tuesday /

_____ : _____ _____
_____ : _____ _____
_____ : _____ _____
_____ : _____ _____
_____ : _____ _____

Wednesday /

_____ : _____ _____
_____ : _____ _____
_____ : _____ _____
_____ : _____ _____
_____ : _____ _____

Thursday /

_____ : _____ _____
_____ : _____ _____
_____ : _____ _____
_____ : _____ _____
_____ : _____ _____

Friday /

_____ : _____ _____
_____ : _____ _____
_____ : _____ _____
_____ : _____ _____
_____ : _____ _____

Mom's Goals :

_____

_____

_____

Kid's Goals :

_____

_____

_____

Top 4 To-Do :

1 _____

2 _____

3 _____

4 _____

_____

_____

_____

_____

_____

_____

_____

_____

_____

_____

_____

Meal Planner

Mon

Tue

Wed

Thu

Fri

Sat

Sun

Weekend

Saturday

_____

_____

_____

_____

_____

Sunday

_____

_____

_____

_____

_____

Monday /

_____ : _____   _____

_____ : _____   _____

_____ : _____   _____

_____ : _____   _____

_____ : _____   _____

Tuesday /

_____ : _____   _____

_____ : _____   _____

_____ : _____   _____

_____ : _____   _____

_____ : _____   _____

Wednesday /

_____ : _____   _____

_____ : _____   _____

_____ : _____   _____

_____ : _____   _____

_____ : _____   _____

Thursday /

_____ : _____   _____

_____ : _____   _____

_____ : _____   _____

_____ : _____   _____

_____ : _____   _____

Friday /

_____ : _____   _____

_____ : _____   _____

_____ : _____   _____

_____ : _____   _____

_____ : _____   _____

Mom's Goals :

_____

_____

_____

Kid's Goals :

_____

_____

_____

Top 4 To-Do :

1 _____

2 _____

3 _____

4 _____

_____

_____

_____

_____

_____

_____

_____

_____

_____

Meal Planner

Mon

Tue

Wed

Thu

Fri

Sat

Sun

Weekend

Saturday

_____

_____

_____

_____

Sunday

_____

_____

_____

_____

Monday   /

_____ : _____   _____

_____ : _____   _____

_____ : _____   _____

_____ : _____   _____

_____ : _____   _____

Tuesday   /

_____ : _____   _____

_____ : _____   _____

_____ : _____   _____

_____ : _____   _____

_____ : _____   _____

Wednesday   /

_____ : _____   _____

_____ : _____   _____

_____ : _____   _____

_____ : _____   _____

_____ : _____   _____

Thursday   /

_____ : _____   _____

_____ : _____   _____

_____ : _____   _____

_____ : _____   _____

Friday   /

_____ : _____   _____

_____ : _____   _____

_____ : _____   _____

_____ : _____   _____

_____ : _____   _____

Mom's Goals :

_____

_____

_____

Kid's Goals :

_____

_____

_____

Top 4 To-Do :

1 _____

2 _____

3 _____

4 _____

_____

_____

_____

_____

_____

_____

_____

_____

_____

_____

Meal Planner

Mon

Tue

Wed

Thu

Fri

Sat

Sun

Weekend

Saturday

_____

_____

_____

_____

_____

Sunday

_____

_____

_____

_____

_____

KAHOOTIE CO.

Monday /

_____ : _____ _____
_____ : _____ _____
_____ : _____ _____
_____ : _____ _____
_____ : _____ _____

Tuesday /

_____ : _____ _____
_____ : _____ _____
_____ : _____ _____
_____ : _____ _____
_____ : _____ _____

Wednesday /

_____ : _____ _____
_____ : _____ _____
_____ : _____ _____
_____ : _____ _____

Thursday /

_____ : _____ _____
_____ : _____ _____
_____ : _____ _____
_____ : _____ _____

Friday /

_____ : _____ _____
_____ : _____ _____
_____ : _____ _____
_____ : _____ _____

Mom's Goals :

_____

_____

_____

Kid's Goals :

_____

_____

_____

Top 4 To-Do :

1 _____

2 _____

3 _____

4 _____

_____

_____

_____

_____

_____

_____

_____

_____

_____

_____

_____

Meal Planner

Mon

Tue

Wed

Thu

Fri

Sat

Sun

Weekend

Saturday

_____

_____

_____

_____

_____

Sunday

_____

_____

_____

_____

_____

Monday /

_____ : _____ _____

_____ : _____ _____

_____ : _____ _____

_____ : _____ _____

_____ : _____ _____

Tuesday /

_____ : _____ _____

_____ : _____ _____

_____ : _____ _____

_____ : _____ _____

_____ : _____ _____

Wednesday /

_____ : _____ _____

_____ : _____ _____

_____ : _____ _____

_____ : _____ _____

_____ : _____ _____

Thursday /

_____ : _____ _____

_____ : _____ _____

_____ : _____ _____

_____ : _____ _____

_____ : _____ _____

Friday /

_____ : _____ _____

_____ : _____ _____

_____ : _____ _____

_____ : _____ _____

_____ : _____ _____

Mom's Goals :

_____

_____

_____

Kid's Goals :

_____

_____

_____

Top 4 To-Do :

1 _____

2 _____

3 _____

4 _____

_____

_____

_____

_____

_____

_____

_____

_____

_____

_____

Meal Planner

Mon

Tue

Wed

Thu

Fri

Sat

Sun

Weekend

Saturday

_____

_____

_____

_____

_____

Sunday

_____

_____

_____

_____

_____

Monday /

_____ : _____

_____ : _____

_____ : _____

_____ : _____

_____ : _____

Tuesday /

_____ : _____

_____ : _____

_____ : _____

_____ : _____

_____ : _____

Wednesday /

_____ : _____

_____ : _____

_____ : _____

_____ : _____

_____ : _____

Thursday /

_____ : _____

_____ : _____

_____ : _____

_____ : _____

_____ : _____

Friday /

_____ : _____

_____ : _____

_____ : _____

_____ : _____

Mom's Goals :

_____

_____

_____

Kid's Goals :

_____

_____

_____

Top 4 To-Do :

Meal Planner

1 _____

2 _____   Mon

3 _____

4 _____   Tue

☐ _____

☐ _____   Wed

☐ _____

☐ _____   Thu

☐ _____

☐ _____   Fri

☐ _____

☐ _____   Sat

☐ _____

☐ _____   Sun

☐ _____

Weekend

Saturday

_____

_____

_____

_____

_____

Sunday

_____

_____

_____

_____

_____

Monday /

_____ : _____

_____ : _____

_____ : _____

_____ : _____

_____ : _____

Tuesday /

_____ : _____

_____ : _____

_____ : _____

_____ : _____

_____ : _____

Wednesday /

_____ : _____

_____ : _____

_____ : _____

_____ : _____

_____ : _____

Thursday /

_____ : _____

_____ : _____

_____ : _____

_____ : _____

_____ : _____

Friday /

_____ : _____

_____ : _____

_____ : _____

_____ : _____

_____ : _____

Mom's Goals :

_____
_____
_____

Kid's Goals :

_____
_____
_____

Top 4 To-Do :

1 _____
2 _____
3 _____
4 _____

_____
_____
_____
_____
_____
_____
_____
_____
_____
_____
_____

Meal Planner

Mon

Tue

Wed

Thu

Fri

Sat

Sun

Weekend

Saturday

_____
_____
_____
_____
_____

Sunday

_____
_____
_____
_____
_____

Monday   /

_____ : _____   _____
_____ : _____   _____
_____ : _____   _____
_____ : _____   _____
_____ : _____   _____

Tuesday   /

_____ : _____   _____
_____ : _____   _____
_____ : _____   _____
_____ : _____   _____
_____ : _____   _____

Wednesday   /

_____ : _____   _____
_____ : _____   _____
_____ : _____   _____
_____ : _____   _____
_____ : _____   _____

Thursday   /

_____ : _____   _____
_____ : _____   _____
_____ : _____   _____
_____ : _____   _____
_____ : _____   _____

Friday   /

_____ : _____   _____
_____ : _____   _____
_____ : _____   _____
_____ : _____   _____
_____ : _____   _____

Mom's Goals :

_____
_____
_____

Kid's Goals :

_____
_____
_____

Top 4 To-Do :

1 _____
2 _____
3 _____
4 _____

_____
_____
_____
_____
_____
_____
_____
_____
_____
_____
_____

Meal Planner

Mon

Tue

Wed

Thu

Fri

Sat

Sun

Weekend

Saturday

_____
_____
_____
_____
_____

Sunday

_____
_____
_____
_____
_____

Monday /

_____ : _____   _____
_____ : _____   _____
_____ : _____   _____
_____ : _____   _____
_____ : _____   _____

Tuesday /

_____ : _____   _____
_____ : _____   _____
_____ : _____   _____
_____ : _____   _____
_____ : _____   _____

Wednesday /

_____ : _____   _____
_____ : _____   _____
_____ : _____   _____
_____ : _____   _____
_____ : _____   _____

Thursday /

_____ : _____   _____
_____ : _____   _____
_____ : _____   _____
_____ : _____   _____
_____ : _____   _____

Friday /

_____ : _____   _____
_____ : _____   _____
_____ : _____   _____
_____ : _____   _____
_____ : _____   _____

Mom's Goals :

_____
_____
_____

Kid's Goals :

_____
_____
_____

Top 4 To-Do :

1 _____
2 _____
3 _____
4 _____

_____
_____
_____
_____
_____
_____
_____
_____
_____
_____
_____
_____

Meal Planner

Mon

Tue

Wed

Thu

Fri

Sat

Sun

Weekend

Saturday

_____
_____
_____
_____
_____

Sunday

_____
_____
_____
_____
_____

KAHOOTIE CO.

Monday /

_____ : _____

_____ : _____

_____ : _____

_____ : _____

_____ : _____

Tuesday /

_____ : _____

_____ : _____

_____ : _____

_____ : _____

_____ : _____

Wednesday /

_____ : _____

_____ : _____

_____ : _____

_____ : _____

_____ : _____

Thursday /

_____ : _____

_____ : _____

_____ : _____

_____ : _____

_____ : _____

Friday /

_____ : _____

_____ : _____

_____ : _____

_____ : _____

_____ : _____

Mom's Goals :

_____

_____

_____

Kid's Goals :

_____

_____

_____

Top 4 To-Do :

Meal Planner

1 _____

2 _____

Mon

3 _____

4 _____

Tue

_____

_____

Wed

_____

_____

Thu

_____

_____

Fri

_____

_____

Sat

_____

_____

Sun

_____

_____

Weekend

Saturday

Sunday

_____   _____

_____   _____

_____   _____

_____   _____

Monday   /

_____ : _____   _____
_____ : _____   _____
_____ : _____   _____
_____ : _____   _____
_____ : _____   _____

Tuesday   /

_____ : _____   _____
_____ : _____   _____
_____ : _____   _____
_____ : _____   _____
_____ : _____   _____

Wednesday   /

_____ : _____   _____
_____ : _____   _____
_____ : _____   _____
_____ : _____   _____
_____ : _____   _____

Thursday   /

_____ : _____   _____
_____ : _____   _____
_____ : _____   _____
_____ : _____   _____

Friday   /

_____ : _____   _____
_____ : _____   _____
_____ : _____   _____
_____ : _____   _____

Mom's Goals :

_____

_____

_____

Kid's Goals :

_____

_____

_____

Top 4 To-Do :

1 _____

2 _____

3 _____

4 _____

_____

_____

_____

_____

_____

_____

_____

_____

_____

_____

Meal Planner

Mon

Tue

Wed

Thu

Fri

Sat

Sun

Weekend

Saturday

_____

_____

_____

_____

_____

Sunday

_____

_____

_____

_____

_____

KAHOOTIE CO.

Monday /

_____ : _____ _____

_____ : _____ _____

_____ : _____ _____

_____ : _____ _____

_____ : _____ _____

Tuesday /

_____ : _____ _____

_____ : _____ _____

_____ : _____ _____

_____ : _____ _____

_____ : _____ _____

Wednesday /

_____ : _____ _____

_____ : _____ _____

_____ : _____ _____

_____ : _____ _____

_____ : _____ _____

Thursday /

_____ : _____ _____

_____ : _____ _____

_____ : _____ _____

_____ : _____ _____

_____ : _____ _____

Friday /

_____ : _____ _____

_____ : _____ _____

_____ : _____ _____

_____ : _____ _____

_____ : _____ _____

Mom's Goals :

_____

_____

_____

Kid's Goals :

_____

_____

_____

Top 4 To-Do :

1 _____

2 _____

3 _____

4 _____

_____

_____

_____

_____

_____

_____

_____

_____

_____

_____

_____

_____

_____

Meal Planner

Mon

Tue

Wed

Thu

Fri

Sat

Sun

Weekend

Saturday

_____

_____

_____

_____

_____

Sunday

_____

_____

_____

_____

_____

Monday /

_____ : _____ _____

_____ : _____ _____

_____ : _____ _____

_____ : _____ _____

_____ : _____ _____

Tuesday /

_____ : _____ _____

_____ : _____ _____

_____ : _____ _____

_____ : _____ _____

_____ : _____ _____

Wednesday /

_____ : _____ _____

_____ : _____ _____

_____ : _____ _____

_____ : _____ _____

_____ : _____ _____

Thursday /

_____ : _____ _____

_____ : _____ _____

_____ : _____ _____

_____ : _____ _____

_____ : _____ _____

Friday /

_____ : _____ _____

_____ : _____ _____

_____ : _____ _____

_____ : _____ _____

_____ : _____ _____

Mom's Goals :

_____
_____
_____

Kid's Goals :

_____
_____
_____

Top 4 To-Do :

1 _____
2 _____
3 _____
4 _____

_____
_____
_____
_____
_____
_____
_____
_____
_____
_____

Meal Planner

Mon

Tue

Wed

Thu

Fri

Sat

Sun

Weekend

Saturday

_____
_____
_____
_____
_____

Sunday

_____
_____
_____
_____
_____

Monday /

____ : _____ _____

____ : _____ _____

____ : _____ _____

____ : _____ _____

____ : _____ _____

Tuesday /

____ : _____ _____

____ : _____ _____

____ : _____ _____

____ : _____ _____

____ : _____ _____

Wednesday /

____ : _____ _____

____ : _____ _____

____ : _____ _____

____ : _____ _____

____ : _____ _____

Thursday /

____ : _____ _____

____ : _____ _____

____ : _____ _____

____ : _____ _____

____ : _____ _____

Friday /

____ : _____ _____

____ : _____ _____

____ : _____ _____

____ : _____ _____

____ : _____ _____

Mom's Goals :

_____

_____

_____

Kid's Goals :

_____

_____

_____

Top 4 To-Do :

1 _____

2 _____

3 _____

4 _____

_____

_____

_____

_____

_____

_____

_____

_____

_____

_____

_____

Meal Planner

Mon

Tue

Wed

Thu

Fri

Sat

Sun

Weekend

Saturday

_____

_____

_____

_____

_____

Sunday

_____

_____

_____

_____

_____

Monday /

_____ : _____ _____

_____ : _____ _____

_____ : _____ _____

_____ : _____ _____

_____ : _____ _____

Tuesday /

_____ : _____ _____

_____ : _____ _____

_____ : _____ _____

_____ : _____ _____

_____ : _____ _____

Wednesday /

_____ : _____ _____

_____ : _____ _____

_____ : _____ _____

_____ : _____ _____

_____ : _____ _____

Thursday /

_____ : _____ _____

_____ : _____ _____

_____ : _____ _____

_____ : _____ _____

_____ : _____ _____

Friday /

_____ : _____ _____

_____ : _____ _____

_____ : _____ _____

_____ : _____ _____

_____ : _____ _____

Mom's Goals :

_____

_____

_____

Kid's Goals :

_____

_____

_____

Top 4 To-Do :

1 _____

2 _____

3 _____

4 _____

_____

_____

_____

_____

_____

_____

_____

_____

_____

_____

Meal Planner

Mon

Tue

Wed

Thu

Fri

Sat

Sun

Weekend

Saturday

_____

_____

_____

_____

_____

Sunday

_____

_____

_____

_____

_____

KAHOOTIE CO.

Monday   /

_____ : _____   _____

_____ : _____   _____

_____ : _____   _____

_____ : _____   _____

_____ : _____   _____

Tuesday   /

_____ : _____   _____

_____ : _____   _____

_____ : _____   _____

_____ : _____   _____

_____ : _____   _____

Wednesday   /

_____ : _____   _____

_____ : _____   _____

_____ : _____   _____

_____ : _____   _____

_____ : _____   _____

Thursday   /

_____ : _____   _____

_____ : _____   _____

_____ : _____   _____

_____ : _____   _____

_____ : _____   _____

Friday   /

_____ : _____   _____

_____ : _____   _____

_____ : _____   _____

_____ : _____   _____

_____ : _____   _____

Mom's Goals :

_____

_____

_____

Kid's Goals :

_____

_____

_____

Top 4 To-Do :

1 _____

2 _____

3 _____

4 _____

_____

_____

_____

_____

_____

_____

_____

_____

_____

_____

_____

Meal Planner

Mon

Tue

Wed

Thu

Fri

Sat

Sun

Weekend

Saturday

_____

_____

_____

_____

_____

Sunday

_____

_____

_____

_____

_____

Monday   /

_____ : _____   _____
_____ : _____   _____
_____ : _____   _____
_____ : _____   _____
_____ : _____   _____

Tuesday   /

_____ : _____   _____
_____ : _____   _____
_____ : _____   _____
_____ : _____   _____
_____ : _____   _____

Wednesday   /

_____ . _____   _____
_____ : _____   _____
_____ : _____   _____
_____ : _____   _____
_____ : _____   _____

Thursday   /

_____ : _____   _____
_____ : _____   _____
_____ : _____   _____
_____ : _____   _____
_____ : _____   _____

Friday   /

_____ : _____   _____
_____ : _____   _____
_____ : _____   _____
_____ : _____   _____
_____ : _____   _____

Mom's Goals :

_____

_____

_____

Kid's Goals :

_____

_____

_____

Top 4 To-Do :

1 _____

2 _____

3 _____

4 _____

_____

_____

_____

_____

_____

_____

_____

_____

_____

_____

Meal Planner

Mon

Tue

Wed

Thu

Fri

Sat

Sun

Weekend

Saturday

_____

_____

_____

_____

_____

Sunday

_____

_____

_____

_____

_____

Monday /

_____ : _____

_____ : _____

_____ : _____

_____ : _____

_____ : _____

Tuesday /

_____ : _____

_____ : _____

_____ : _____

_____ : _____

_____ : _____

Wednesday /

_____ : _____

_____ : _____

_____ : _____

_____ : _____

_____ : _____

Thursday /

_____ : _____

_____ : _____

_____ : _____

_____ : _____

_____ : _____

Friday /

_____ : _____

_____ : _____

_____ : _____

_____ : _____

_____ : _____

Mom's Goals :

_____

_____

_____

Kid's Goals :

_____

_____

_____

Top 4 To-Do :

Meal Planner

1 _____

2 _____   Mon

3 _____

4 _____   Tue

_____

_____   Wed

_____

_____   Thu

_____

_____   Fri

_____

_____   Sat

_____

_____   Sun

_____

Weekend

Saturday

Sunday

_____   _____

_____   _____

_____   _____

_____   _____

_____   _____

Monday /

____ : _____ _____

____ : _____ _____

____ : _____ _____

____ : _____ _____

____ : _____ _____

Tuesday /

____ : _____ _____

____ : _____ _____

____ : _____ _____

____ : _____ _____

____ : _____ _____

Wednesday /

____ : _____ _____

____ : _____ _____

____ : _____ _____

____ : _____ _____

____ : _____ _____

Thursday /

____ : _____ _____

____ : _____ _____

____ : _____ _____

____ : _____ _____

Friday /

____ : _____ _____

____ : _____ _____

____ : _____ _____

____ : _____ _____

____ : _____ _____

Mom's Goals :

_____

_____

_____

Kid's Goals :

_____

_____

_____

Top 4 To-Do :

1 _____

2 _____

3 _____

4 _____

_____

_____

_____

_____

_____

_____

_____

_____

_____

_____

Meal Planner

Mon

Tue

Wed

Thu

Fri

Sat

Sun

Weekend

Saturday

_____

_____

_____

_____

_____

Sunday

_____

_____

_____

_____

_____

KAHOOTIE CO.

Monday   /

_____ : _____   _____
_____ : _____   _____
_____ : _____   _____
_____ : _____   _____
_____ : _____   _____

Tuesday   /

_____ : _____   _____
_____ : _____   _____
_____ : _____   _____
_____ : _____   _____
_____ : _____   _____

Wednesday   /

_____ : _____   _____
_____ : _____   _____
_____ : _____   _____
_____ : _____   _____
_____ : _____   _____

Thursday   /

_____ : _____   _____
_____ : _____   _____
_____ : _____   _____
_____ : _____   _____
_____ : _____   _____

Friday   /

_____ : _____   _____
_____ : _____   _____
_____ : _____   _____
_____ : _____   _____
_____ : _____   _____

Mom's Goals :

_____

_____

_____

Kid's Goals :

_____

_____

_____

Top 4 To-Do :

1 _____

2 _____

3 _____

4 _____

_____

_____

_____

_____

_____

_____

_____

_____

_____

_____

_____

Meal Planner

Mon

Tue

Wed

Thu

Fri

Sat

Sun

Weekend

Saturday

_____

_____

_____

_____

_____

Sunday

_____

_____

_____

_____

_____

Monday   /

_____ : _____   _____

_____ : _____   _____

_____ : _____   _____

_____ : _____   _____

_____ : _____   _____

Tuesday   /

_____ : _____   _____

_____ : _____   _____

_____ : _____   _____

_____ : _____   _____

_____ : _____   _____

Wednesday   /

_____ : _____   _____

_____ : _____   _____

_____ : _____   _____

_____ : _____   _____

_____ : _____   _____

Thursday   /

_____ : _____   _____

_____ : _____   _____

_____ : _____   _____

_____ : _____   _____

_____ : _____   _____

Friday   /

_____ : _____   _____

_____ : _____   _____

_____ : _____   _____

_____ : _____   _____

Mom's Goals :

_____
_____
_____

Kid's Goals :

_____
_____
_____

Top 4 To-Do :

1 _____
2 _____
3 _____
4 _____

_____
_____
_____
_____
_____
_____
_____
_____
_____
_____
_____
_____
_____

Meal Planner

Mon

Tue

Wed

Thu

Fri

Sat

Sun

Weekend

Saturday

_____
_____
_____
_____

Sunday

_____
_____
_____
_____

Monday /

_____ : _____ _____

_____ : _____ _____

_____ : _____ _____

_____ : _____ _____

_____ : _____ _____

Tuesday /

_____ : _____ _____

_____ : _____ _____

_____ : _____ _____

_____ : _____ _____

_____ : _____ _____

Wednesday /

_____ : _____ _____

_____ : _____ _____

_____ : _____ _____

_____ : _____ _____

_____ : _____ _____

Thursday /

_____ : _____ _____

_____ : _____ _____

_____ : _____ _____

_____ : _____ _____

_____ : _____ _____

Friday /

_____ : _____ _____

_____ : _____ _____

_____ : _____ _____

_____ : _____ _____

_____ : _____ _____

Mom's Goals :

_____
_____
_____

Kid's Goals :

_____
_____
_____

Top 4 To-Do :

1 _____
2 _____
3 _____
4 _____

_____
_____
_____
_____
_____
_____
_____
_____
_____
_____
_____
_____

Meal Planner

Mon

Tue

Wed

Thu

Fri

Sat

Sun

Weekend

Saturday

_____
_____
_____
_____
_____

Sunday

_____
_____
_____
_____
_____

KAHOOTIE CO.

Made in the USA
Middletown, DE
22 May 2022

66061355R00076